For Nick and Matt.
H.E

For my brother, who has taken care
of me since we were little and still does,
though from a distance.

A.L

LITTLE TIGER
LONDON

CATERPILLAR BOOKS
An imprint of the Little Tiger Group • www.littletiger.co.uk
1 Coda Studios, 189 Munster Road, London SW6 6AW
First published in Great Britain 2020 • Text by Harriet Evans
Text copyright © Caterpillar Books Ltd 2020
Illustrations copyright © Andrés Landazábal 2020
A CIP catalogue record for this book is available
from the British Library
All rights reserved • Printed in China
ISBN: 978-1-84857-945-3
CPB/1400/1344/1219
1 3 5 7 9 10 8 6 4 2

Brothers

Families are different,
with brothers **big** and small,

Stepbrothers

or half-brothers,

we **love** them, one and all.

They'll be there on your **worst** days

to help you dry your eyes.

They'll be there on your **best** days,
when your heart soars to the skies.

A brand **new** baby brother

to take under your wing

Is a rare and **precious** present,

an unsung song to sing.

You might find your brothers in the **friends** you make.

Sailing on **adventures**, your bond will never break.

Brothers make life **messy**

and upset the best-laid plans,

But they'll remain beside you,
a pair of **helping hands**.

Big brothers lift you up, they teach you all they know;

A **playmate** and a **mentor**, to help you as you grow.

Always wearing
hand-me-downs

can soon get tired and old,

But sharing has its upsides,
like **trust** and **secrets** told.

Brothers might annoy you
and sometimes make you scream,

But when you work together,
you make the **perfect team**.

Brothers will **support** your dreams
and who you want to be.
Though you may be opposites,

He's
the **sky**...

...to your **deep sea**.

Families are different,

with brothers **big** and small,

Stepbrothers or half-brothers...

...we **love** them...

...one and all.